GREAT MINDS® WIT & WISDOM

Grade 5 Module 3:
A War Between Us

Student Edition

Table of Contents

Handout 27A: Focusing Question Task 3 Journal Entry Planner

Handout 28A: Oral Rehearsal Summary and Feedback

Handout 28B: "The Women Who Went to the Field" Poem

Handout 29A: Content Vocabulary: *consolers*

Handout 30A: Fluency Homework

Handout 31A: Delphine's Analogy

Handout 33A: End-of-Module Task Evidence Organizer

Handout 35A: Howard's Understanding

Handout 36A: End-of-Module Task Essay Planner

Handout 36B: End-of-Module Task Exemplar Opinion Essay

Handout 37A: Opinion Writing Checklist

Volume of Reading Reflection Questions

Wit & Wisdom Parent Tip Sheet

Name: _____

Date: _____

Handout 1A: Vocabulary Words from "What Caused the Civil War"

Directions: Practice the module's Listening Goal by paying attention to words you are familiar with to define the less familiar words in the first column. As you listen to the video, jot down words and examples in the second column that help you better understand each word. After the video, develop a definition for each word in the final column.

Unfamiliar Word	Familiar Words from the Video	Definition
industrial (adj.)		
agricultural (adj.)		
abolished (v.)		
secede (v.)		
Union (n.)		
Confederate (adj.)		

Name: _____

Date: _____

Handout 1B: Prefix *anti-*

Part 1: Match the word below with the correct definition by writing the word in the blank space next to the definition.

anti-aging   antibody   antiflu   antifreeze

Word	Definition
	A medicine used to prevent flu.
	A protein made by the body that works with other proteins to destroy toxic substances in the body.
	A product to prevent the appearance of getting older.
	A product that lowers the freezing point of liquids.

Part 2: Complete the sentence stem.

1.   The doctor prescribed an *antiflu* drug because _____

_____.

2.   A flu shot contains an *antibody* that _____

_____.

3.   People purchase *anti-aging* products because _____

_____.

4.   My dad bought *antifreeze* for the car because _____

_____.

Name: _____

Date: _____

Handout 1C: Assessed Vocabulary Study Guide

Directions: Use this list of vocabulary words and definitions to study for the Vocabulary Assessment. The number following the word indicates the lesson number in which the word or affix is taught.

Words/Affixes (Lesson Numbers)	Definitions
-able (6)	Can or able to be.
-cour- (14)	Run.
-ped- (16)	Foot, feet.
abolished (1)	Gotten rid of.
absently (30)	Showing a person is distracted and thinking about something else.
agricultural (1)	Having to do with farming.
aliens (22)	Those who live in a country who are not citizens of that country.
amputated (11)	To cut off.
anti- (1)	Against.
civil (1)	Having to do with the activities of people who are members of a country.
Confederate (1)	Having to do with the southern states that separated from the United States, or Union.
consolers (29)	Comforters.
enlist (7)	To join; to sign up to serve in the military.
futile (31)	Useless.
idle (20)	Not working, not active.
industrial (1)	Having to do with producing items.
landmark (22)	A feature of the landscape that is easy to see and recognize.

Name: _____

Date: _____

mutilate (11)	To destroy by cutting off a needed part.
naïve (13)	Lacking knowledge or experience.
primitive (11)	Simple, or not developed.
quagmire (25)	A swamp or marsh.
reality (8)	Truth.
recruitment (7)	The process of getting someone to join a group.
secede (1)	To break away.
slavery (1)	The owning of a person by another person.
sober (23)	Serious, solemn.
succor (22)	Assistance; help given during a time of need.
tignon (32)	Headdress worn by Creole women of Louisiana.
transfixed (20)	Fascinated; held motionless (as in wonder or astonishment).
Union (1)	Northern states that stayed under a single government.

Name: _____

Date: _____

Handout 2A: Differences Between the North and South

Directions: After viewing a map showing differences between the North and the South in 1861, complete the following table by (a) indicating which section of the country benefitted the most from the differences displayed in the map, and (b) explaining how that section of the country benefitted from the difference. In answer to the last question on this handout, explain which section of the country had the greatest advantage going into the start of the Civil War based on the differences.

Map Title	Which section of the country benefitted from this difference?	How did the North or South benefit from this difference?
Free Population		
Slave Population		

Name: _____

Date: _____

Manufacturing		
Agriculture		
Each section of the country benefitted in its own way from these differences. Which section of the country had the ultimate advantage going into the start of the Civil War? Why?		

Name: _____

Date: _____

Handout 2B: Prefix *ab-*

Directions: Match the word with the sentence in which the word belongs by correctly filling in the blanks.

abduct   abolish   abscond   absent   abstain

1.   Many people wanted to _____ slavery.

2.   How many days have you been _____ from school this year?

3.   "The Ransom of Red Chief" by O. Henry is about two men who _____ a banker's son.

4.   The thief wanted to _____ with the money before anyone knew the money was missing.

5.   Jim decided to _____ from watching TV during the week because it interfered with his school work.

Name: _____

Date: _____

Handout 4A: Speaking and Listening Structure Checklist

Directions: Evaluate your participation by marking + for "yes" and Δ for "not yet" in the appropriate boxes. Ask someone (adult or peer) to evaluate your participation as well.

Speaking and Listening Structure Checklist			
	Self +/ Δ	Peer +/ Δ	Teacher +/ Δ
I asked questions to understand better what a speaker was saying.			
I answered questions that others asked me in order to clarify ideas.			
I used my notes and evidence to organize my thoughts while speaking.			
I summarized a speaker's point before adding on my own ideas by either agreeing or disagreeing, giving an example, or elaborating.			
I listened for context clues to make sense of what a speaker was saying.			
Total number of +'s:			

Name: _____

Date: _____

Handout 7A: Exemplar Opinion Essay

Directions: Read the following prompt and opinion essay.

Prompt: Young boys were banned from enlisting to fight in the Civil War, but they enlisted anyway. Should it have been harder for boys to enlist in the Civil War? Use evidence from *The Boys' War* to develop two reasons, and elaborate on your opinion.

Exemplar Opinion Essay:

Imagine a boy, just twelve years old, sneaking away from his family in the middle of the night to enlist to fight in a war. In *The Boys' War*, Jim Murphy states that many boys fought and died during the Civil War. Boys weren't allowed to enlist to fight in the Civil War, but many were able to anyway. It should have been harder for boys to enlist to fight in the Civil War. They didn't understand the seriousness of the war and they hurt their families needlessly.

The first reason why it should have been harder for boys to enlist in the Civil War is that they didn't understand the seriousness of war. The text says some boys thought going off to war would be "all fun and frolic" (Murphy 8). Other boys wanted to prove a point and take "...the defiant South and 'set them straight'" (Murphy 8). This shows that war was like a game to these boys. They didn't understand that war is serious business where people die and lives are torn apart. Boys had no right to sign up to fight in a war when they thought it was going to be a fun adventure. Boys weren't ready for the realities of war and it should have been harder for them to sneak in and enlist.

The second reason why it should have been harder for boys to enlist in the Civil War is that they hurt their families needlessly. For example, Elisha Stockwell told his sister he was going into town for an errand. He didn't come home for two years because he had actually snuck off to join the war (Murphy 13). This matters because boys hurt their families a lot by lying to them. For two years, Elisha's family was left wondering what had happened to him. If it had been harder for boys to enlist to fight in the war, then Elisha's family would have never had to feel the pain they did for two years. By enlisting to fight in the war, boys lied and hurt their families.

In conclusion, boys weren't ready to be part of the war. It should have been much harder for them to enlist to fight in it.

Name: _____

Date: _____

Handout 7B: Opinion Essay Reverse Outline

Directions: Read the exemplar opinion essay on Handout 7A. Then, use your knowledge of essay structure to fill in the following rows with the correct information from the exemplar opinion essay.

Introduction Paragraph		
H	Hook	Imagine a boy, just twelve years old, sneaking away from his family in the middle of the night to enlist to fight in a war.
I	Introduce	In *The Boys' War*, Jim Murphy states that many boys fought and died during the Civil War. Boys weren't allowed to enlist to fight in the Civil War, but many were able to anyway.
O	**Opinion Statement**	Opinion Statement:

Reason 1:		Reason 2:

Name: _____

Date: _____

	Body Paragraph 1	
R	**Reason**	
E	Evidence	The text says some boys thought going off to war would be "all fun and frolic" (Murphy 8). Other boys wanted to prove a point and take "...the defiant South and 'set them straight'" (Murphy 8).
E	Elaboration	This shows that war was like a game to these boys. They didn't understand that war is serious business where people die and lives are torn apart. Boys had no right to sign up to fight in a war when they thought it was going to be a fun adventure.
C	Concluding Statement	Boys weren't ready for the realities of war and it should have been harder for them to sneak in and enlist.

	Body Paragraph 2		
R	**Reason**	Transition from Reason 1, and	state Reason 2.
E	Evidence	For example, Elisha Stockwell told his sister he was going into town for an errand. He didn't come home for two years because he had actually snuck off to join the war (Murphy 13).	
E	Elaboration	This matters because boys hurt their families a lot by lying to them. For two years, Elisha's family was left wondering what had happened to him. If it had been harder for boys to enlist to fight in the war, then Elisha's family would have never had to feel the pain they did for two years.	
C	Concluding Statement	By enlisting to fight in the war, boys lied and hurt their families.	

Name: _____

Date: _____

Concluding Paragraph		
O	**Opinion**	

Name: _____

Date: _____

Handout 7C: Fluency Homework

Directions:

1. Day 1: Read the text carefully and annotate to help you read fluently.
2. Each day:
   a. Practice reading the text three to five times.
   b. Evaluate your progress by placing a √+, √, or √- in each unshaded box.
   c. Ask someone (adult or peer) to listen and evaluate you as well.
3. Last day: Respond to the self-reflection questions.

Generally, boys from the North did not join the army because they felt a burning desire to stamp out slavery. One boy's comment about slavery is fairly typical: "I do not know anything about it, whether it is a good thing or a bad thing," he wrote in a letter, "and when talk gets around to it I say very little." Many joined because they wanted to take the defiant South and "set them straight." But most signed up for a simpler reason—to escape the boring routine of farm life and take part in an exciting adventure.

The same spirit of adventure and glory motivated Southern boys as well. A Mississippi recruit said he had joined "to fight the Yankies—all fun and frolic." But underneath the festive attitude was another, deeply felt reason for serving—to defend their homes from a large invading army. One Southern boy made his feelings clear, "I reather die then be com a Slave to the North."

Murphy, Jim. *The Boys' War: Confederate and Union Soldiers Talk About the Civil War*. Houghton Mifflin Company, 1990, p. 8.

Name: _____

Date: _____

Student Performance Checklist:	Day 1		Day 2		Day 3		Day 4	
	You	Listener*	You	Listener*	You	Listener*	You	Listener*
Accurately read the passage 3–5 times.								
Read with appropriate phrasing and pausing.								
Read with appropriate expression.								
Read articulately at a good pace and an audible volume.								

*Adult or peer

Self-reflection: What choices did you make when deciding how to read this passage, and why? What would you like to improve on or try differently next time? (*Thoughtfully answer these questions on this paper.*)

Name: _____

Date: _____

Handout 7D: Suffixes -*ate* and -*ation*

Directions: Add the definitions for *humiliated* and *motivated* to the first column, and add the -*ation* forms of *humiliated* and *motivated* to the third column along with the part of speech and definition. In the last column, write an original sentence with the -*ation* form. You will add two words to the last two rows and fill in the columns for those words in Lesson 11.

-ate: "to make or do"	Sentence from the text	-ation: "the results of making"	Sentence
activate (v.): "to make something start working"	The switch on the wall will *activate* the light.	activation (n.): "the results of making something active"	Susan forgot the *activation* code for the alarm and could not turn it on.
humiliated (v.):	"My father was there and objected to my going, so they scratched my name out, which *humiliated* me somewhat" (11).		
motivated (v.):	"The same spirit of adventure and glory *motivated* Southern boys as well" (8).		

Name: _____

Date: _____

Handout 8A: Soldiers' Points of View

Directions: Read the following summaries of how soldiers experienced two different aspects of the war. Then, read soldiers' firsthand accounts and write an inference about each soldier's point of view, or opinion, on that aspect of the war. Finally, explain how the soldiers' points of view were similar and/or different

Aspect of War: Uniforms	
Both sides in the Civil War needed matching uniforms.	
Northern Soldier's Firsthand Account:	**Southern Soldier's Firsthand Account:**
"'...my trousers were too long by three or four inches; the shirt was coarse and unpleasant, too large at the neck and too short elsewhere. The cap was an ungainly bag with pasteboard top and leather visor; while the overcoat made me feel like a little nubbin of corn in a large husk. Nothing ever took down my ideas of military pomp quite so low.'" (Murphy 17)	"'I was not very tall and caps and drawers were in short supply, so they went to the older, bigger men. I did not mind this and was happy with what I had, which was what I had brought from home, until the sergeant came to me and said, 'Do you want to be taken for a...Yankee in all that blue?' I did not, so after each fight I would search the field for anyone near my size who did not require use of his equipment. I must confess to feeling very bad doing this, believing the dead should not be disturbed...but I had no other course. In just a few weeks my uniform was the equal of anyone's.'" (18)
Infer this soldier's point of view (feelings, opinion):	**Infer this soldier's point of view (feelings, opinion):**

Name:

Date:

Are these soldiers' points of view similar or different? Why?

Name: _____

Date: _____

Aspect of War: Officers

Both sides in the Civil War had officers who were responsible for training soldiers and maintaining discipline and order in the camp.

Northern Soldier's Firsthand Account:	**Southern Soldier's Firsthand Account:**
"'The first day I went out to drill, getting tired of doing the same things over and over, I said to the drill-sergeant, 'Let's stop this fooling and go over to the grocery.' His only reply was addressed to the corporal: 'Corporal, take this man out and drill him like hell.' And the corporal did! I found that suggestions were not well appreciated in the army as in private life…It takes a raw recruit some time to learn that he is not to think or suggest, but obey.'" (21)	"A private from Georgia wrote an angry letter home about a new rule that required men to remove their hats when they went to the general's tent: 'You know that is one thing I wont do. I would rather see him in hell before I will pull off my hat to any man and tha Jest as well shoot me at the start.'" (21–22)
Infer this soldier's point of view (feelings, opinion):	**Infer this soldier's point of view (feelings, opinion):**

Name: _____

Date: _____

Are these soldiers' points of view similar or different? Why?

Name: _____

Date: _____

Handout 8B: Perfect Tense Identification

Directions: Highlight or circle the verbs in each sentence. Label each verb as present, past, future, present perfect, past perfect, or future perfect tense.

1.   We have not taken our exams yet.

   _____

2.   My best friend had already seen the movie I wanted to see.

   _____

3.   By Saturday, I will have waited one week to see the new movie.

   _____

4.   I regretted that I had not studied more for my test.

   _____

5.   Sara has been to the library twice this week.

   _____

Name: _____

Date: _____

Handout 9A: Perfect Tense

Directions: Choose one verb from the list below and write one question using that verb in the present perfect tense on the lines provided. Then write an answer to the question.

Example: *sleep* <u>Have</u> you ever <u>slept</u> until noon? Yes, I <u>have slept</u> until noon.
send <u>Has</u> your cousin ever <u>sent</u> you a text? No, my cousin <u>has</u> never <u>sent</u> me a text.

eat	fish	swim
bring	talk	play
help	dance	sing
catch	hear	watch
listen	go	see
wish	visit	live
run	fly	meet

1. Question:

_____

_____

2. Answer:

_____

_____

Name: _____

Date: _____

Part 2

Directions: Circle two of the verbs listed above. Use one of the verbs to a write sentence with a past perfect tense verb and one of the verbs to write a sentence with a future perfect tense verb. Underline or highlight the verbs.

1.   Past perfect tense:

_____

_____

2.   Future perfect tense:

_____

_____

Part 3

Directions: Read the sentence and the verb tense in parentheses following it. Complete the sentence by writing a verb in the required tense in the blank.

1.   I _____ lunch at the same time every day this week.
      (present perfect tense)

2.   By 5:00 P.M. yesterday, I _____ already
      _____ my homework. (past perfect tense)

3.   By the time we finish reading *The Boys' War*, I _____ six
      books this year. (present perfect tense)

Name: _____

Date: _____

Handout 11A: Civil War Medicine

Directions: Read the following summary of Civil War medicine, another aspect of war. Then, read the firsthand accounts and write an inference about each person's point of view, or opinion, on Civil War medicine. Finally, explain how these points of view are similar and/or different.

Aspect of War: Civil War medicine

Doctors' knowledge of medicine and treatments for wounded soldiers was primitive during the Civil War.

Soldier from "Hospitals and Medical Knowledge."	Soldier from *The Boys' War:*	Surgeon from "Amputation."
"...corporal drew his revolver on a doctor, saying, 'The man that puts a hand on me dies'" (Hardtack and Coffee, 310).	"I believe the Doctors kills more than they cour. Doctors haint Got half Sence" (Murphy 88).	"...the shattering, splintering, and splitting of a long bone...were, in many instances, both remarkable and frightful, and early experiences taught surgeons that amputation was the only means of saving a life" (Tenting Tonight, 92).
Infer this soldier's point of view (feelings, opinion):	**Infer this soldier's point of view (feelings, opinion):**	**Infer this surgeon's point of view (feelings, opinion):**
Are these three points of view similar, different, or both? Why?		

Name: _____

Date: _____

Handout 12A: Focusing Question Task 2 Evidence Organizer

Directions: Choose the best evidence to develop your reasons and opinion statement. Follow the prompts at the top of the chart to write brief notes in the boxes below.

Prompt: Write an opinion essay in which you explain whether being a soldier in the Civil War affected boys for the better or for the worse. Use evidence from *The Boys' War* to develop two reasons. Elaborate on your evidence to support your reasons.

Opinion Statement:

Reason	Evidence	Elaboration/Explanation
Why do you have the opinion you have? What reason supports your opinion?	List evidence from the text that supports your reason. Include the page number.	What does this evidence prove about the impact of war? How does this information show that boy soldiers have been affected for the better or for the worse?

Name:

Date:

Reason	Evidence	Elaboration/Explanation
Why do you have the opinion you have? What reason supports your opinion?	List evidence from the text that supports your reason. Include the page number.	What does this evidence prove about the impact of war? How does this information show that boy soldiers have been affected for the better or for the worse?

Name: _____

Date: _____

Handout 13A: Soldiers' Changes

Directions: Read the following aspect of war. Then, read the firsthand accounts and write an inference about each soldier's point of view, or opinion, on that aspect of war. Finally, explain how these points of view are similar and/or different.

Aspect of War: Boy soldiers experiencing battle.

John Delhaney:	Thomas Galway:	Elisha Stockwell:	
"Now we are over a fence and the [line] we are to charge is right ahead…the bullets whistle thro' the leaves and ears and send many brave comrade to his last account. But we have no time to think; such is the excitement, such the feeling with which I am inspired that I rush on with the rest, completely bewildered and scarcely heeding what takes place around" (Murphy 71).	"Our ammunition is running low. The order is passed along the line for us to charge. There are no bugles to sound it, but we look at one another and, fixing our bayonets, we raise a cheer and go forward" (Murphy 71).	"I want to say, as we lay there and the shells were flying over us, my thought went back to my home, and I thought what a foolish boy I was to run away and get into such a mess I was in. I would have been glad to have seen my father coming after me" (Murphy 33).	
Infer this soldier's point of view (feelings, opinion):	**Infer this soldier's point of view (feelings, opinion):**	**Infer this soldier's point of view (feelings, opinion):**	
	Are these soldiers' points of view similar, different, or both? Why?		

Name:

Date:

Aspect of War: Boy soldiers witnessing death during battles.

Thomas Galway:	Unidentified soldier:	Henry Graves:
"We passed over the old battlefield of Manassas. The rains of two years have uncovered many of the shallow graves. Bony knees, long toes, and grinning skulls are to be seen in all directions. In one place I saw a man's boot protruding from the grave…Horrid sights are, to an old soldier, horrid no longer" (Murphy 72–73).	"We are aroused early on the 16th by a shell which exploded over the regimental colors, killing Corporal Farmer, the color bearer. A piece of the shell literally cut him in two. But we cooked our breakfast and chatted as usual. Some of the men even gambled" (Murphy 75).	"I saw the body of a man killed the previous day this morning and a horrible sight it was. Such sights do not effect me as they once did. I can not describe the change nor do I know when it took effect, yet I know that there is a change for I look on the carcass of a man with pretty much the same feeling as I would do were it a horse or hog" (Murphy 75).
Infer this soldier's point of view (feelings, opinion):	**Infer this soldier's point of view (feelings, opinion):**	**Infer this soldier's point of view (feelings, opinion):**
Are these soldiers' points of view similar, different, or both? Why?		

Name: _____

Date: _____

Handout 13B: Fluency Homework

Directions:

1. Day 1: Read the text carefully and annotate to help you read fluently.
2. Each day:
   a. Practice reading the text three to five times.
   b. Evaluate your progress by placing a √+, √, or √- in each unshaded box.
   c. Ask someone (adult or peer) to listen and evaluate you as well.
3. Last day: Respond to the self-reflection questions.

Fighting in a war changes any soldier, but it especially changed the boys who fought in the Civil War. When they had enlisted, they were naïve, undisciplined, and used to doing farm-related chores. Given several months of drilling and experience in battle, these boys had turned into true soldiers. Granted, they would never have the spit and polish to impress anyone while on parade, but their skill in the field had been honed to a killing edge.

The fear and confusion that often gripped them in the early fighting gave way to a cooler, more analytical head. In the smoke and roar and chaos of battle, these boys would now hold their lines, obey drum commands, and listen for orders. And when a command was issued, they had learned to follow it even in the face of enemy fire.

Murphy, Jim. *The Boys' War: Confederate and Union Soldiers Talk About the Civil War.* Houghton Mifflin Company, 1990, p. 67..

Name: _____

Date: _____

Student Performance Checklist:	Day 1		Day 2		Day 3		Day 4	
	You	Listener*	You	Listener*	You	Listener*	You	Listener*
Accurately read the passage 3–5 times.								
Read with appropriate phrasing and pausing.								
Read with appropriate expression.								
Read articulately at a good pace and an audible volume.								

*Adult or peer

Self-reflection: What choices did you make when deciding how to read this passage, and why? What would you like to improve on or try differently next time? (*Thoughtfully answer these questions on this paper.*)

Name: _____

Date: _____

Handout 13C: The Meaning of *naïve*

Directions: With a partner, complete the last two columns of this table by adding a character's name and an example of the character's naïve behavior. The first row has been completed for you.

Naïve character in a...	[Naïve character's name] in [Title]	Example of naïve behavior
Movie	Pinocchio in *Pinocchio*	Pinocchio believes Honest John and Gideon are his friends, but they force him into show business.
Movie		
Book		
Cartoon		
Television show		
Fairy tale or fable		

Name: _____

Date: _____

Handout 15A: Focusing Question Task 2 Essay Planner

Directions: Use this planner to develop and organize ideas for your opinion essay. Write in complete sentences in the following boxes to create your draft response to Focusing Question Task 2.

Introduction

Hook (H)	How will you "hook" your audience, or catch their attention?
Introduce (I)	Introduce your topic. Provide any necessary background information or context for your topic.
Opinion Statement (O)	State your opinion.

Reason 1	Reason 2

Name: _____

Date: _____

Supporting Paragraph 1—Reason 1:

Reason R)	State the first reason that supports your opinion.
Evidence (E)	Cite evidence that develops Reason 1, including any necessary context.
Elaboration (E)	Explain how the evidence develops Reason 1.
Concluding Statement (C)	Close your paragraph.

Name: _____

Date: _____

Supporting Paragraph 2—Reason 2:

_____

Reason R)	Transition from your first reason, and state the second reason that supports your opinion.
Evidence (E)	Cite evidence that develops Reason 2, including any necessary context:.
Elaboration (E)	Explain how the evidence supports Reason 2..
Concluding Statement (C)	Close your paragraph.

Name:

Date:

Conclusion

	Reinforce your opinion.
Opinion (O)	Reflect on the importance of your opinion. What do you want your reader to remember about how war affected boy soldiers?

Name: _____

Date: _____

Handout 17A: Fluency Homework

Directions:

1. Day 1: Read the text carefully and annotate to help you read fluently.
2. Each day:
   a. Practice reading the text three to five times.
   b. Evaluate your progress by placing a √+, √, or √– in each unshaded box.
   c. Ask someone (adult or peer) to listen and evaluate you as well.
3. Last day: Respond to the self-reflection questions.

A bunch of local boys met up after their work, pretending to soldier. You couldn't get many boys to stick up for U.S. Grant and the North that April. Only the Henson boys and Gideon Hickman and Jack Popejoy. And Noah.

You could hear them from up here, barking out their raggedy commands: "Draw saber! By the right flank, quick trot, march!" Like they knew all about it....

...Down the road by the old stone structure that served as a schoolhouse, a bigger bunch of boys drilled. But they drilled for the South and Jeff Davis....

They'd divvied up, some for the North, more for the South. Why didn't they just fight it out right here in the road, fair and square? Did they even know it could end with them killing one another in some godforsaken loblolly far from home? I couldn't get my mind around it, and I'd always thought I understood Noah. We were twins, and I swore I could hear his heart beat.

Peck, Richard. *The River Between Us*. 2003. Puffin Books, 2005, pp. 25–26.

Name: _____

Date: _____

Student Performance Checklist:	Day 1		Day 2		Day 3		Day 4	
	You	Listener*	You	Listener*	You	Listener*	You	Listener*
Accurately read the passage 3–5 times.								
Read with appropriate phrasing and pausing.								
Read with appropriate expression.								
Read articulately at a good pace and an audible volume.								

*Adult or peer

Self-reflection: What choices did you make when deciding how to read this passage, and why? What would you like to improve on or try differently next time? (*Thoughtfully answer these questions on this paper.*)

Name: _____

Date: _____

Handout 18A: Tilly's Point of View of Delphine and Calinda

Directions: As you reread pages 34–39 of *The River Between Us*, record Tilly's observations about Delphine and Calinda. Then, describe Tilly's point of view of these two young women. Finally, explain how Tilly's life experiences influence her point of view of Delphine and Calinda, and how her point of view is reflected in her description of these characters in chapter 3.

Tilly's observations about Delphine: (Record two or three key details.)	**Tilly's observations about Calinda:** (Record two or three key details.)

Describe Tilly's point of view, or feelings, about Delphine and Calinda. *How does she react to these new characters? What is her impression of them?* Cite one to two pieces of evidence from pages 34–39 to support your ideas.

Name: _____

Date: _____

Consider what you have learned about Tilly's and her family's life in Grand Tower. How do you think Tilly's life experiences influence her point of view of Delphine and Calinda?

_____

_____

_____

_____

How is Tilly's point of view reflected in her description of Delphine and Calinda in chapter 3? Support your response with textual evidence

_____

_____

_____

_____

Name: _____

Date: _____

Handout 18B: Different Dialects

Directions: Complete the chart by locating examples of Delphine's dialect, explaining what the author means, and rewriting how someone else might say it differently. An example has been done for you. Then, answer the question at the bottom of this handout.

What did the author say?	What did the author mean?	How might someone say it differently?
"Il est saoul!"	He is drunk.	He's as drunk as a skunk.

Name:

Date:

How do Delphine's and Tilly's dialects differ?

Name: _____

Date: _____

Handout 19A: Character Detective

Directions: Reread the breakfast table scene on pages 45–50. Then, make inferences about Delphine and/or Calinda based on evidence in this scene. For each piece of evidence listed below, write your inference(s) about Delphine and/or Calinda. What does each piece of evidence reveal about these characters' traits, their thoughts or feelings, or their background?

Evidence of characters' words, and/or actions	My Inference(s): *What does this evidence reveal about Delphine and/or Calinda, including their traits, thoughts, feelings, or background?*
Page 46: "I leaned in to pour brimming cups of sassafras tea. Calinda bent to sniff at her cup and flinched. Overlooking her eggs, Delphine said, 'How good you are to take us in, orphans of the storm.' Her smile was like sunup. Across from me, Calinda eyed the scrapple with dark suspicion. She poked at and egg with her fork."	Example: *I infer from this evidence that Calinda has probably never had this kind of tea and food. She doesn't seem to trust it.* *This evidence also suggests that Delphine is cheerful and polite. I can't tell how she feels about the food, but it seems important to her to show good manners.*
Page 47: "Mama stepped in, so to speak. 'Won't your aunt up at St. Louis wonder what become of you?' Calinda shot a quick sideways glance at Delphine, who answered at once. 'Tante Blanche! Of course, unless she is already murder in her bed. I write at once to say where we are.'"	

Name: _____

Date: _____

Page 49: "Delphine turned over a tiny, plump hand. 'But war may not come to us. New Orleans is the largest city of the South, perhaps the greatest in the world. It could strangle the North by blocking ships to the river's mouth.' She knotted up her fist and held it up. 'New York will do anything to keep our cotton coming. New York does not care who picks it.'"	
Page 49: "[Delphine] leaned nearer, to take us into her confidence. 'Maman is a lady of fashion, you know. To our house on Chartres Street come all the persons of tone, all the distinguished.'"	
Pages 49–50: "[Delphine] caught her breath at her mother's magnificence. 'Tall as a swaying palmetto is Maman, the belle of ev'ry ball…They cannot hold the opera on Wednesday nights. Clemence Duvall is at the ball! The balls, you know, each Wednesday at the Salle d'Orleans.'" Something happened then. Below the table Calinda's hand seemed to jerk at Delphine's skirts. Delphine fell silent. A warning had passed between them."	

Name: _____

Date: _____

Page 50: "Delphine wavered and went on. 'No, Maman will not leave her Nouvelle Orleans. Not yet. Perhaps never. Perhaps we can all be as we were.' She looked away from us, seeming to hear music."	

Name: _____

Date: _____

Handout 19B: Dialect Compare and Contrast

Part 1

Directions: Each passage in Part 1 is spoken by one of the Pruitts. Rewrite the passage in Delphine's dialect.

1. "It's happenin', dadburn it!" (42)

_____

_____

2. "Girl, I'd like to turn you every way but loose." (43)

_____

_____

3. "And your folks down South, won't they fret about your whereabouts?" (48)

_____

_____

Name: _____

Date: _____

Part 2

Directions: Each passage in Part 2 is spoken by Delphine. Rewrite the passage in the Pruitts' dialect.

4. *"Mais oui, madame,* we stuff petticoats around the windows." (46)

_____

_____

5. *"Tante Blanche!* Of course, unless she is already murder in her bed." (47)

_____

_____

6. "Tall as a swaying palmetto is Maman, the belle of ev'ry ball." (49)

_____

_____

Name: _____

Date: _____

Handout 20A: Exemplar Opinion Paragraph from Tilly's Point of View

Directions: Read the following prompt and opinion paragraph written from the first-person point of view of Tilly Pruitt from *The River Between Us*.

Prompt: At the end of chapter 5, Tilly calls Delphine and Calinda "light bringers," because not only have they brought oil lamps to brighten the house, but they have brought excitement and pleasure into the Pruitt family's lives as well. How might Tilly support her opinion that Delphine and Calinda are "light bringers?" Write a paragraph from Tilly's first-person point of view, using evidence from the story to develop your opinion with at least one reason, and elaborate on your opinion.

When I first saw Delphine and Calinda step off the steamboat, I had no idea how my life would change. Delphine and Calinda truly are light bringers! Ever since they arrived, my life feels more exciting and far less ordinary than it used to. Going into town, for example, is not something I usually look forward to. "Town" consists of just a few stores along our dirt Front Street, and we don't have much money to spend. But today, Delphine lent me one of her fine bonnets to wear. This made me feel so ladylike and fancy, kind of like Delphine herself! She also bought coal oil lamps and boxes of matches at Jenkins' store. We've never had any light in our home except for the light from the fireplace. When darkness fell, the light from the lamps was marvelous. Mama, Cass, and I kept looking at each other and wondering if we were living someone else's life! I am so thankful that Delphine and Calinda landed in Grand Tower and joined our family. Until they arrived, every day felt dull and the same as the one before. Delphine and Calinda have only been with us for a day and already they have brought so much excitement and pleasure into our lives.

Name: _____

Date: _____

Handout 21A: Fluency Homework

Directions:

1. Day 1: Read the text carefully and annotate to help you read fluently.
2. Each day:
   a. Practice reading the text three to five times.
   b. Evaluate your progress by placing a √+, √, or √- in each unshaded box.
   c. Ask someone (adult or peer) to listen and evaluate you as well.
3. Last day: Respond to the self-reflection questions.

There weren't many quiet moments in Delphine's vicinity, but now you could hear voices from town, and the river lapping the bank. We sat there with our skirttails tucked under us. At last she said, "You are relieve it is the lamp boy who goes, and not Noah."

She read my heart aright. It was one of her talents. Sorry though I was to see Curry go, I could have burst into song right where we set that it wasn't Noah going. Not yet.

Somehow my heart could spare Curry. If war had never come—if Delphine had never come—it might have been different. But war took Curry away. And Delphine made me begin to look around myself, and farther from myself. I didn't know what to make of that great world she come from, but she made me want more in my small one. And so Curry and me wasn't to be.

Peck, Richard. *The River Between Us*. 2003. Puffin Books, 2005, pp. 69-70..

Name: _____

Date: _____

Student Performance Checklist:	Day 1		Day 2		Day 3		Day 4	
	You	Listener*	You	Listener*	You	Listener*	You	Listener*
Accurately read the passage 3–5 times.								
Read with appropriate phrasing and pausing.								
Read with appropriate expression.								
Read articulately at a good pace and an audible volume.								

*Adult or peer

Self-reflection: What choices did you make when deciding how to read this passage, and why? What would you like to improve on or try differently next time? (*Thoughtfully answer these questions on this paper.*)

Name: _____

Date: _____

Handout 22A: Tilly's Opinion Planner

Directions: Like Mama, Tilly does not regret that Delphine and Calinda have come. Use the planner below to help you think about how Tilly might express this opinion from her point of view, and what reason(s) and evidence she might use to support her opinion. Like Mama, Tilly's reason(s) should be based on the positive changes she sees in herself as a result of Delphine's influence.

Remember, when you express an opinion from a character's point of view, you:

- **Pretend you are the character!** Don't write about the character; write as if you are the character! (Challenge: Consider how the character speaks in the story, and try to imitate his or her voice in your writing.)

- **Use the first person.** Use words like I, me, my, our, and us, referring to the character, not yourself.

- **State the character's opinion in his or her voice.** The character's opinion should be stated in or inferred from the story.

- **Support the character's opinion using actual evidence from the story.** Find and use evidence from the story to back up your character's opinion and reason(s).

Opinion statement	*State Tilly's opinion in response to her own question: "Do you wish Delphine and Calinda had never come?"*	

Name:

Date:

Reason *Give a reason to support this opinion, based on the positive changes that Tilly sees in herself.*	**Evidence** *Cite one to two pieces of evidence that Tilly might give for this reason, including necessary context. (Remember to write this evidence in Tilly's voice.)*

Name: _____

Date: _____

Handout 22B: Appropriate and Inappropriate Shifts in Tense

Directions: Read the following excerpt from *The River Between Us*. The **bolded** verbs are examples of appropriate verb tenses for this passage. For each underlined verb, determine whether it is an example of an appropriate or inappropriate shift in tense. Write the correct tense of the verb above each underlined verb. Note that some underlined verbs may already be in the correct tense.

"Mama **pretended** surprise to see them, as if she <u>spends</u> a summer day in her shoes and a fresh apron.

'Mrs. Pruitt,' Mrs. Manfred Cady <u>is saying</u> 'it is hot weather and a hard climb, and we **are** all busy women, preparin' for war.'

She <u>fetched</u> up a shuddering breath, and Mama <u>says</u> calmly, 'I am up for the day myself.'

'We won't take more than a moment of your time,' Mrs. Jenkins said, and in they <u>will come</u>, looking around as if they'd never <u>sat</u> foot here before."

Name: _____

Date: _____

Handout 23A: Calinda's Dance

Directions: Consider the effect that Calinda's dance has on Tilly, on Delphine, and on Calinda herself. In the left-hand column, describe how Calinda's dance affects each of these three characters. In the right-hand column, record evidence from Tilly's description on pages 91–94 that helps you understand how Calinda's dance affects these characters, from Tilly's point of view. Finally, answer the reflection questions in the last box.

What effect does Calinda's dance have on...	Evidence
...Tilly?	How do you know? What details from Tilly's description on pages 91–94 help you understand the effect Calinda's dance has on Tilly and how it makes her feel?
...Delphine?	How do you know? What details from Tilly's description of Delphine on pages 91–94 help you understand the effect that Calinda's dance has on Delphine and how it makes her feel?
...Calinda herself?	How do you know? What details from Tilly's description of Calinda on pages 91–94 help you understand the effect that dancing has on Calinda and how it makes her feel?

Name:

Date:

Reflection: Until this point in the story, Calinda has remained a mysterious character, to the Pruitts as well as to readers. How does witnessing Calinda dancing in this scene change Tilly's point of view of Calinda? What more does Delphine reveal about Calinda in this scene? What questions do you still have about both Calinda and Delphine after reading this scene?

Name: _____

Date: _____

Handout 24A: Exemplar Journal Entry from Tilly's Point of View

Directions: Read the following prompt and journal entry from Tilly's point of view. Notice that the second body paragraph of this journal entry is only partially written. Later, you will develop this paragraph with evidence from the story.

Prompt: How does Tilly feel about her brother joining up as a soldier in the army? Based on what you have read so far, what opinion do you think Tilly would have about her brother's decision to go off to the war? Pretend you are Tilly. Write a journal entry from Tilly's point of view, expressing her opinion about whether Noah should have left her family to enlist as a Civil War soldier. State Tilly's opinion and then support it with two reasons and evidence from the story.

Exemplar Response:

Dear Journal,

It's late, and I can't sleep. Ever since Noah left, all I can think about is him. Noah should never have left us and joined up to fight this war. First of all, war is real and deadly. Secondly, Noah's leaving has destroyed Mama.

Noah, Curry, and all these other boys from Grand Tower seem to think this war is a big adventure, but it is not. War is real, and it is deadly. The war had hardly begun before the boys in our town were out in the streets playing like they were soldiers and taking prisoners. (Peck 25–26). They acted like it was all a big game, with some of them for the North and some of them for the South. None of them seem to realize that in real war, Northern soldiers kill Southern soldiers and vice-versa. In real war, they could end up killing one of the boys they grew up with. Over what? Cass has had visions of young boys dying in this war. When she first told me about her visions of boys "blown apart, blue and gray," I thought she meant they had drowned (Peck 24). But now I realize she meant boy soldiers, North and South. Cass didn't see excitement and glory. She saw suffering and death. I have never seen war, but I know enough to know that too many people will die.

Name: _____

Date: _____

While I fear for Noah's life, I worry that Mama will never be the same either. Noah's leaving has destroyed her.

_____

_____

_____

_____

_____

_____

Noah and I used to be so close. But ever since this war started, I can't understand him. I just know he should never have gone off to fight. I wish I could have convinced him to stay here in Grand Tower with us. The only thing I can do now is hope that he comes home alive.

Yours truly,

Tilly

Name: _____

Date: _____

Handout 24B: Fluency Homework

Directions:

1. Day 1: Read the text carefully and annotate to help you read fluently.
2. Each day:
   a. Practice reading the text three to five times.
   b. Evaluate your progress by placing a √+, √, or √- in each unshaded box.
   c. Ask someone (adult or peer) to listen and evaluate you as well.
3. Last day: Respond to the self-reflection questions.

The cold of the floor climbed my legs. My heart was frozen. I reeled at how quick my life had come to an end. I couldn't go, and I couldn't stay.

I didn't doubt that Noah was sick. He'd have the trots by now, the way they were eating. We'd heard about the pneumonia the boys had brought with them from the wet ground they'd slept on at Jacksonville. We knew about the measles, and there was typhoid talk. Dr. Hutchings had said Cairo was a pesthole.

But how could I go? I didn't know where the world was, nor how to get there.

Peck, Richard. *The River Between Us*. 2003. Puffin Books, 2005, p. 101.

Name: _____

Date: _____

Student Performance Checklist:	Day 1		Day 2		Day 3		Day 4	
	You	Listener*	You	Listener*	You	Listener*	You	Listener*
Accurately read the passage 3–5 times.								
Read with appropriate phrasing and pausing.	▒	▒						
Read with appropriate expression.	▒	▒	▒	▒				
Read articulately at a good pace and an audible volume.	▒	▒	▒	▒	▒	▒		

*Adult or peer

Self-reflection: What choices did you make when deciding how to read this passage, and why? What would you like to improve on or try differently next time? (*Thoughtfully answer these questions on the back of this paper.*)

Name: _____

Date: _____

Handout 25A: Tilly's and Delphine's Points of View

Directions: Consider how Tilly and Delphine each feel about the idea of traveling to Cairo to find Noah and about traveling on the train. For each character, infer her feelings about the topic, using the page numbers designated below. Be sure to cite one to two details from the text to support your ideas for each character. Finally, answer the questions about the differences between Tilly's and Delphine's feelings regarding the trip to Cairo.

Tilly's Feelings	Topic	Delphine's Feelings
How does Tilly feel about the idea of traveling to Cairo, based on her description on pages 102–104?		How does Delphine feel about the idea of traveling to Cairo, based on Tilly's description of her words and actions on pages 102–103?
	The idea of traveling to Cairo to find Noah	
The best detail(s) that show Tilly's feelings include:		The best detail(s) that show Delphine's feelings include:

Name:

Date:

How does Delphine feel about traveling on the train, based on Tilly's description of her words and actions on pages 105–106?

The best detail(s) that show Delphine's feelings include:

Traveling on the train

How does Tilly feel about traveling on the train, based on her description on pages 105–106?

The best detail(s) that show Tilly's feelings include:

Name: _____

Date: _____

How do Tilly's and Delphine's feelings differ when it comes to the journey to Cairo—the idea of it and the actual journey itself? Write your answer in one or two sentences.

_____

_____

_____

_____

_____

Why do you think their feelings differ? What experiences in each of their lives might have influenced their points of view about such a journey? Write your answer in two or three sentences.

_____

_____

_____

_____

_____

Name: _____

Date: _____

Handout 26A: Character Change Chart

Directions: For each character, describe what she was like earlier in the story, before coming to Cairo and Camp Defiance, and what she is like now. How has each young woman changed? Provide evidence—one or two quotations and a page number—to support your descriptions of the characters before and now. Finally, in the center column, explain what caused Tilly's and Delphine's changes.

Tilly Before
Describe what Tilly was like earlier in the story, before coming to Cairo and Camp Defiance.

Tilly Now
Describe what Tilly is like now, since coming to Cairo and Camp Defiance. How has she changed?

What Caused This Change?
How did the war, and coming to Cairo and Camp Defiance, help bring about this change?

Evidence of Tilly Before			Evidence of Tilly Now	
Page #	Quotation		Page #	Quotation

Name: _____

Date: _____

Delphine Before

Describe what Delphine was like earlier in the story, before coming to Cairo and Camp Defiance.

Delphine Now

Describe what Delphine is like now, since coming to Cairo and Camp Defiance. How has she changed?

Evidence of Delphine Before	
Page #	Quotation

What Caused This Change?

How did the war, and coming to Cairo and Camp Defiance, help bring about this change?

Evidence of Delphine Now	
Page #	Quotation

Name: _____

Date: _____

Handout 27A: Focusing Question Task 3 Journal Entry Planner

Directions: Use this planner to develop and organize ideas for your journal entry from Tilly's point of view. For this task, your journal entry should follow the same basic structure as an opinion essay. Write in complete sentences in the following boxes to create your draft response to Focusing Question Task 3. Remember to write as if you are Tilly, from her first-person point of view.

Introduction

Hook (H)	How will you "hook" your audience, or catch their attention?
Introduce (I)	Introduce your topic. Provide any necessary background information or context for your topic.
Opinion Statement (O)	State Tilly's opinion about how the war and the experiences in Cairo and at Camp Defiance have changed her and Delphine.

Reason 1 – how Tilly herself has changed	Reason 2 – how Delphine has changed

Name: _____

Date: _____

Supporting Paragraph 1–Reason 1: (about Tilly)

Reason R)	State the first reason–about Tilly's own change–that supports Tilly's opinion.
Evidence (E)	Give evidence of what Tilly was like before to develop Reason 1, including any necessary context.
Elaboration (E)	Explain how the evidence develops Reason 1.
Evidence (E)	Give evidence of what Tilly is like now to develop Reason 1, including any necessary context.
Elaboration (E)	Explain how the evidence develops Reason 1.
Concluding Statement (C)	Close your paragraph.

Name: _____

Date: _____

Supporting Paragraph 2–Reason 2: (about Delphine)

Reason R)	Transition from your first reason, and state the second reason–about Delphine's change–that supports Tilly's opinion.
Evidence (E)	Give evidence of what Delphine was like before to develop Reason 2, including any necessary context.
Elaboration (E)	Explain how the evidence develops Reason 2..
Evidence (E)	Give evidence of what Delphine was like before to develop Reason 2, including any necessary context.
Elaboration (E)	Explain how the evidence develops Reason 2..
Concluding Statement (C)	Close your paragraph.

Name:

Date:

Conclusion

Opinion (O)	Reinforce Tilly's opinion.
	Reflect, from Tilly's point of view, on the importance of this opinion about how she and Delphine have changed. What might she take away from her experiences of the war and in Cairo and Camp Defiance?

Name: _____

Date: _____

Handout 28A: Oral Rehearsal Summary and Feedback

Directions:

1.   Listen to your partner orally rehearse his or her opinion statement with two reasons and supporting paragraphs. If it is helpful, take notes as you listen to help you make sense of what your partner is saying.

2.   After listening to each part, summarize the reasons your partner gives to support Tilly's opinion or, for the supporting paragraphs, the evidence he/she gives to support each reason.

3.   Record any feedback or suggestions for your partner based on what you hear. If needed, ask your partner to rehearse his or her writing a second time.

Opinion Statement with Two Reasons

Notes as I listen:
The two reasons I heard my partner give to support Tilly's opinion are: •   Reason 1:   •   Reason 2:
My feedback or suggestions include:

Name: _____

Date: _____

Supporting Paragraph 1:

Notes as I listen:
The evidence I heard my partner give to support Tilly's first reason includes:
My feedback or suggestions include:

Supporting Paragraph 2:

Notes as I listen:
The evidence I heard my partner give to support Tilly's second reason includes:
My feedback or suggestions include:

Name: _____

Date: _____

Handout 28B: "The Women Who Went to the Field" Poem

Directions:

1.   Read the poem silently. Refer to the glossary to define or find more information about unknown words and phrases in the poem.

2.   Read the poem aloud, practicing decoding each word accurately.

3.   Read the poem again, aloud or silently. Use the space to the right of the poem to "notice and wonder," recording any observations or questions you have about the poem.

	The Women Who Went to the Field by Clara Barton
1	The women who went to the field, you say,
	The women who went to the field; and pray
	What did they go for? just to be in the way!–
	They'd not know the difference betwixt[1] work and play,
5	What did they know about war anyway?
	What could they do? – of what use could they be?
	They would scream at the sight of a gun, don't you see?
	Just fancy them round where the bugle notes play,
10	And the long roll is bidding us on to the fray[2].
	Imagine their skirts 'mong artillery[3] wheels,
	And watch for their flutter as they flee 'cross the fields
	When the charge is rammed home and the fire belches hot;–
	They never will wait for the answering shot.
	They would faint at the first drop of blood, in their sight.

[1] betwixt: between
[2] fray: battle
[3] artillery: large weapons used in land battles, such as cannons

Name: _____

Date: _____

15	What fun for us boys, – (ere[4] we enter the fight;)
	They might pick some lint[5], and tear up some sheets,
	And make us some jellies, and send on their sweets,
	And knit some soft socks for Uncle Sam's[6] shoes,
	And write us some letters, and tell us the news.
20	And thus it was settled by common consent[7],
	That husbands, or brothers, or whoever went,
	That the place for the women was in their own homes,
	There to patiently wait until victory comes.
	But later, it chanced, just how no one knew,
25	That the lines slipped a bit, and some 'gan to crowd through;
	And they went, – where did they go? – Ah; where did they not?
	Show us the battle, – the field, – or the spot
	Where the groans of the wounded rang out on the air
	That her ear caught it not, and her hand was not there,
30	Who wiped the death sweat from the cold, clammy brow,
	And sent home the message; – "'T[8] is well with him now"?
	Who watched in the tents, whilst the fever fires burned,
	And the pain-tossing limbs in agony turned,
	And wet the parched tongue, calmed delirium's[9] strife

---

[4] *ere: before*

[5] *pick some lint, and tear up some sheets: During the Civil War, military hospitals were in desperate need of dressings for wounds. People on the homefront—mostly women—contributed to the war by "picking lint" off old clothes and tearing up sheets to use as bandages.*

[6] *Uncle Sam's: a cartoon person that represents the government or the people of the United States. Uncle Sam is a tall, thin man with a beard, top hat, and trousers that have red and white stripes.*

[7] *consent: permission or approval of a plan or action*

[8] *'T: It*

[9] *delirium: a state of mental confusion, caused by high fever or shock*

Name:

Date:

35	Till the dying lips murmured, "My Mother," "My Wife"!...
	...Did these women quail[10] at the sight of a gun?
	Will some soldier tell us of one he saw run?
	Will he glance at the boats on the great western flood,
	At Pittsburgh and Shiloh[11], did they faint at the blood?...
40	...And these were the women who went to the war:
	The women of question; what did they go for?
	Because in their hearts God had planted the seed
	Of pity for woe[12], and help for its need;
	They saw, in high purpose, a duty to do,
45	And the armor of right broke the barriers through.
	Uninvited, unaided, unsanctioned[13] ofttimes[14],
	With pass, or without it, they pressed on the lines;
	They pressed, they implored[15], till they ran the lines through,
	And this was the "running" the men saw them do...
50	...And what would they do if war came again?
	The scarlet cross floats where all was blank then.
	They would bind on their "brassards[16]" and march to the fray,
	And the man liveth not who could say to them nay[17];

[10] quail: to lose courage in difficulty or danger

[11] Shiloh: The Battle of Shiloh, also known as the Battle of Pittsburg Landing, was a major Civil War battle that took place in Tennessee and resulted in a Union victory.

[12] pity for woe: sympathy for another's great suffering or sorrow

[13] unsanctioned: without permission or approval

[14] ofttimes: often times

[15] implored: begged urgently for something

[16] brassards: bands worn on the sleeve, often of a military uniform, to identify those in uniform

[17] liveth: lives

[18] nay: no

Name:

Date:

> They would stand with you now, as they stood with you then,
>
> The nurses, consolers, and saviours of men.

Clara Barton read this poem during a reception on November 18, 1892 at the Willard Hotel in Washington, D.C. Courtesy of the National Park Service.

Name: _____

Date: _____

Handout 29A: Content Vocabulary: *consolers*

Directions: Complete the chart by recording an association such as a person (real or fictional character), a TV show, or an event and by explaining the connection between the word and the association.

Word	Association	Reason/Explanation
nurses		
saviours		
consolers		

Name: _____

Date: _____

Handout 30A: Fluency Homework

Directions:

1. Day 1: Read the text carefully and annotate to help you read fluently.
2. Each day:
   a. Practice reading the text three to five times.
   b. Evaluate your progress by placing a √+, √, or √- in each unshaded box.
   c. Ask someone (adult or peer) to listen and evaluate you as well.
3. Last day: Respond to the self-reflection questions.

She saw me gazing at her arm resting there on the table in the lamplight. I'd always thought her skin was the color of a peach, warmed by the Southern sun.

She drew back her sleeve. "I am nearly as white as you, chère. There are others like me paler than yourself, blue-eyed, yellow-haired. Yet as our saying goes, there is a tignon in the family."

My head whirled, at all this, and her bravery.

"If all is lost for us, I go find another life. Maman, she would give me up to give me my chance. I am her treasure." Tears beaded her lavish lashes. "If it is my fate, I go among those who know nothing, who cannot speak to me as that woman does tonight."

"You were going to St. Louis," I said, "when—"

"Mais non, chère." She shook her head, weary. "I have no aunt. We know no one beyond our world. We free people of color live on a kind of island, lapped by a sea of slavery. Beyond that sea is this territory up here." She gazed around the room. "Like the mountains of the moon to us.

"We would have gone ashore at Cairo because we hear the North begin here. But we take fright when the boat is boarded....

"Your Grand Tower is the next stop of the boat. It is, perhaps, fate?"

And that was something else I didn't know.

Peck, Richard. *The River Between Us*. 2003. Puffin Books, 2005, pp. 129–130.

Name: _____

Date: _____

Student Performance Checklist:	Day 1		Day 2		Day 3		Day 4	
	You	Listener*	You	Listener*	You	Listener*	You	Listener*
Accurately read the passage 3–5 times.								
Read with appropriate phrasing and pausing.								
Read with appropriate expression.								
Read articulately at a good pace and an audible volume.								

*Adult or peer

Self-reflection: What choices did you make when deciding how to read this passage, and why? What would you like to improve on or try differently next time? (*Thoughtfully answer these questions on this paper.*)

Name: _____

Date: _____

Handout 31A: Delphine's Analogy

Directions: Complete the chart with information that helps to explain the analogy Delphine makes on page 130, "We free people of color live on a kind of island, lapped by a sea of slavery."

Literal	Figurative
Free people of color/Delphine	Island
Slavery/slaves	Lapping sea

Sketch an illustration of this analogy. Label its parts.

Name: _____

Date: _____

Handout 33A: End-of-Module Task Evidence Organizer

Directions: Using evidence from *The River Between Us*, record and elaborate on the negative and positive impacts of war for each member of the Pruitt family. Then, use these ideas to inform your opinion for the End-of-Module Task question about the impact of war on the Pruitt family.

Character	War's Negative Impact		War's Positive Impact	
	Evidence:	Elaboration:	Evidence:	Elaboration:
Noah	Evidence:	Elaboration:	Evidence:	Elaboration:

Name: _____

Date: _____

Character	War's Negative Impact				War's Positive Impact			
	Evidence:	Elaboration:	Evidence:	Elaboration:	Evidence:	Elaboration:	Evidence:	Elaboration:
Tilly								

Name: _____

Date: _____

Character	War's Negative Impact		War's Positive Impact	
	Evidence:	Elaboration:	Evidence:	Elaboration:
Ma	Evidence:	Elaboration:	Evidence:	Elaboration:

Name: _____

Date: _____

Character	War's Negative Impact		War's Positive Impact	
	Evidence:	Elaboration:	Evidence:	Elaboration:
	Evidence:	Elaboration:	Evidence:	Elaboration:
Cass				

Name: _____

Date: _____

Handout 35A: Howard's Understanding

Directions: Complete the chart with evidence from the text and your own inferences to explore Howard's deepest understanding of an idea shared by Grandma Tilly.

List the big idea from the novel you want to explore further, from Howard's point of view:

What does Howard learn about this big idea from listening to Grandma Tilly's story? How does he learn this?	What is Howard's deepest understanding of this big idea because of listening to Grandma Tilly's story? Think about how Howard's thoughts or actions may change because of this new understanding.

Name:

Date:

What does Howard's deepest understanding of this idea look like? Draw a picture to represent Howard's deepest understanding. Include a title or caption for your picture.

Name: _____

Date: _____

Handout 36A: End-of-Module Task Essay Planner

Directions: Use this planner to develop and organize ideas for your opinion essay. Write in complete sentences in the following boxes to create your draft response to Focusing Question Task 2.

Introduction

Hook (H)	Use this planner to develop and organize ideas for your opinion essay. Write in complete sentences in the following boxes to create your draft response to the End-of-Module Task.
Introduce (I)	Introduce your topic. Provide any necessary background information or context for your topic.
Opinion Statement (O)	State your opinion.

Reason 1	Reason 2

Name: _____

Date: _____

Supporting Paragraph 1—Reason 1:

_____

Reason R)	State the first reason that supports your opinion.
Evidence (E)	Cite evidence that develops Reason 1, including any necessary context.
Elaboration (E)	Explain how the evidence develops Reason 1.
Concluding Statement (C)	Close your paragraph.

Name: _____

Date: _____

Supporting Paragraph 2—Reason 2:

Reason R)	Transition from your first reason, and state the second reason that supports your opinion.
Evidence (E)	Cite evidence that develops Reason 2, including any necessary context:.
Elaboration (E)	Explain how the evidence supports Reason 2..
Concluding Statement (C)	Close your paragraph.

Name: _____

Date: _____

Conclusion

Opinion (O)	Reinforce your opinion. Reflect on the importance of your opinion. What do you want your reader to remember about how war affected the Pruitt family?

Name: _____

Date: _____

Handout 36B: End-of-Module Task Exemplar Opinion Essay

Directions: Read the following prompt and exemplar opinion essay about the Civil War's impact on Delphine from the historical fiction novel *The River Between Us*.

Prompt: Did the Civil War impact Delphine in a mostly positive or mostly negative way?

Exemplar Opinion Essay:

Imagine what it would feel like to be forced to leave your home and the city you are from and love. In the historical fiction novel, *The River Between Us* by Richard Peck, Delphine, a free person of color from New Orleans, left her home to live in the safety of the North when the Civil War began. Although Delphine didn't fight in the war, it still impacted her. The Civil War had a mostly negative impact on Delphine because she was forced to leave her home and she was never able to be honest about who she was.

First, the Civil War forced Delphine from her home. She met the Pruitts in Grand Tower when she left New Orleans because it was no longer safe for her. In the text, Delphine said, "If all is lost for us, I go find another life. Maman, she would give me up to give me my chance. I am her treasure" (Peck 129). In other words, Delphine had left her family that she loved behind. As a free person of color, she was not going to be safe in the South during the Civil War because to many people in the South, she was just a person of color. They did not care about the "free" part. This shows that the war caused Delphine to make great sacrifices. She left everything she knew and loved for a new, strange place in hopes of having a better life.

Another reason why the Civil War had a mostly negative impact on Delphine is because she was never able to be honest about who she was. At the end of the book, Howard learned that he was Delphine and Noah's grandson. His dad said, "We couldn't be mother and son, you see. She didn't trust the world" (Peck 157). In other words, Delphine hid that she had a child in order to protect him from people who wouldn't approve of her choice to have a child with a white man. If Delphine's way of life had not been threatened by the Civil War, then she would have been able to continue living happily with the custom of plaçage. The war forced Delphine to keep some very big secrets that likely caused her to feel as though she was living a lie.

In conclusion, the Civil War impacted Delphine in a negative way because she lost her home and had to keep secrets from the people she loved most.

Name: _____

Date: _____

Handout 37A: Opinion Writing Checklist

Directions: Use this checklist to revise your writing. Mark + for "yes" and Δ for "not yet." Ask someone (adult or peer) to evaluate your writing as well.

Reading Comprehension	Self +/ Δ	Peer +/ Δ	Teacher +/ Δ
My writing shows I understand the impact of war from the text.			
I use key details from the text to explain the impact of war.			
Structure			
I respond to all parts of the prompt.			
I include a clear opinion statement.			
I use paragraphs to organize information.			
I use linking words and phrases to connect ideas.			
I include concluding statements to conclude my thoughts.			
Development			
I explain my opinion using reasons.			
My evidence is related to my reasons.			
I elaborate upon evidence by explaining it.			
Style			
My writing is appropriate for the purpose and audience of the task.			
Conventions			
I use the correct verb tenses, including perfect verb tenses.			
I use a comma to separate introductory elements from the rest of the sentence.			
Writing Process			
I use an evidence organizer to gather my ideas.			
Total # of +'s			

Volume of Reading Reflection Questions

A War Between Us, Grade 5 Module 3

Student Name: _____

Text: _____

Author: _____

Topic: _____

_____

Genre/type of book: _____

Directions: Share your knowledge about the Civil War by answering the questions below.

Informational Text

1. **Wonder**: How might this text teach you about the Civil War? Provide three details that support your response.

2. **Organize**: What is a main idea of this text? Provide three details that support a main idea.

3. **Reveal**: How does this text compare to others you have read about the Civil War? Describe at least two ways in which the texts are similar and two ways in which they are different.

4. **Distill**: How does this text support or challenge what you already knew about the ways war can impact people? Provide at least three examples.

5. **Know**: How did this text build your knowledge? Explain an important idea about the Civil War, supporting the idea with details from this text.

6. **Vocabulary**: What are three words that specifically relate to some aspect of the Civil War? Use each of these words in a sentence showing the word's connection to the war.

Literary Text:

1. **Wonder**: What drew your attention to this text? How do you think the story might connect to the Civil War?

2. **Organize**: Write a short summary of the story, including the major character(s), setting, problem, and resolution.

3. **Reveal**: Choose one significant quotation by a speaker in the story. How does this quotation give clues as to the speaker's point of view?

4. **Distill**: What is a theme of this story? Provide evidence from the text to support your response.

5. **Know**: How does this literary writing add to your knowledge about the Civil War? Provide specific examples of what you have learned through reading historical fiction.

6. **Vocabulary**: What are three words or phrases from the text that reveal deeper understanding about the Civil War? Explain how each word or phrase helped you to understand the war at a deeper level.

WIT & WISDOM PARENT TIP SHEET

WHAT IS MY GRADE 5 STUDENT LEARNING IN MODULE 3?

Wit & Wisdom is our English curriculum. It builds knowledge of key topics in history, science, and literature through the study of excellent texts. By reading and responding to stories and nonfiction texts, we will build knowledge of the following topics:

Module 1: Cultures in Conflict

Module 2: Word Play

Module 3: A War Between Us

Module 4: Breaking Barriers

In the third module, *A War Between Us*, students are exposed to the many ways in which war impacts people and the many consequences of war. We will read firsthand accounts and historical fiction to answer the question: How did the Civil War impact people?

OUR CLASS WILL READ THESE BOOKS:

Articles

- *"Hospitals and Medical Knowledge," Civil War Preservation Trust*
- *"Amputation," Civil War Preservation Trust*

Historical Account

- *The Boys' War*, Jim Murphy

Novel

- *The River Between Us*, Richard Peck

Poetry

- *"The Women Who Went to the Field,"* Clara Barton

OUR CLASS WILL EXAMINE THESE PHOTOGRAPHS:

- Lincoln at Antietam, Alexander Gardener

OUR CLASS WILL WATCH THESE VIDEOS

- *The Civil War, Episode 1: "The Cause,"* Ken Burns
- "America Divided," History.com
- "What Caused the Civil War," Virginia Historical Society
- "Ford Model T–100 Years Later," CarDataVideo

OUR CLASS WILL VISIT THESE WEB PAGES:

- "Compare Two Worlds: North vs. South 1861," Scholastic.com
- "Slavery," Scholastic.com

OUR CLASS WILL ASK THESE QUESTIONS:

- What factors led to the start of the Civil War?
- How did the Civil War impact boy soldiers?
- How did the Civil War impact girls and women?
- How did the Civil War impact free people of color in the South?
- How did the Civil War impact the Pruitt family from the historical-fiction novel *The River Between Us*?

QUESTIONS TO ASK AT HOME:

As your Grade 5 student reads, ask:

- *What is the essential meaning, or most important message, in this book?*

BOOKS TO READ AT HOME:

- *Civil War Stories,* Ambrose Bierce
- *Chasing Lincoln's Killer,* James Swanson
- *Across Five Aprils,* Irene Hunt
- *With Every Drop of Blood,* James Collier
- *How I Found the Strong,* Margaret McMullan
- *Iron Thunder,* Avi
- *Red Moon at Sharpsburg,* Rosemary Wells
- *The Mostly True Adventures of Homer P. Figg,* Rodman Phillbrick
- *Soldier's Heart,* Gary Paulsen

- *Elijah of Bruxton*, Chrisopher Paul Curtis

- *On Enemy Soil: The Journal of James Edmund Pease, a Civil War Union Soldier*, Jim Murphy

IDEAS FOR TALKING ABOUT THE CIVIL WAR:

Encourage your Grade 5 student to think about both the negative and positive impacts of war as they read, as war changes people in many ways and teaches many lessons. Additionally, invite your Grade 5 student to think about how someone's point of view influences how they describe and react to an event like war.

CREDITS

Great Minds® has made every effort to obtain permission for the reprinting of all copyrighted material. If any owner of copyrighted material is not acknowledged herein, please contact Great Minds® for proper acknowledgment in all future editions and reprints of this module.

- All images are used under license from Shutterstock.com unless otherwise noted.
- For updated credit information, please visit **http://witeng.link/credits**.

ACKNOWLEDGMENTS

Great Minds® Staff

The following writers, editors, reviewers, and support staff contributed to the development of this curriculum.

Ann Brigham, Lauren Chapalee, Sara Clarke, Lorraine Griffith, Emily Gula, Sarah Henchey, Trish Huerster, Lior Klirs, Stephanie Kane-Mainier, Andrea Minich, Lynne Munson, Marya Myers, Rachel Rooney, Aaron Schifrin, Danielle Shylit, Rachel Stack, Sarah Turnage, Amy Wierzbicki, Margaret Wilson, and Sarah Woodard.

Colleagues and Contributors

We are grateful for the many educators, writers, and subject-matter experts who made this program possible.

David Abel, Robin Agurkis, Elizabeth Bailey, Julianne Barto, Amy Benjamin, Andrew Biemiller, Charlotte Boucher, Emily Climer, Jessica Carloni, Sheila Byrd-Carmichael, Janine Cody, Rebecca Cohen, Elaine Collins, Tequila Cornelious, Matt Davis, Beverly Davis, Thomas Easterling, Jeanette Edelstein, Kristy Ellis, Moira Clarkin Evans, Charles Fischer, Marty Gephart, Kath Gibbs, Natalie Goldstein, Christina Gonzalez, Mamie Goodson, Nora Graham, Lindsay Griffith, Brenna Haffner, Joanna Hawkins, Elizabeth Haydel, Steve Hettleman, Cara Hoppe, Ashley Hymel, Carol Jago, Jennifer Johnson, Mason Judy, Gail Kearns, Shelly Knupp, Sarah Kushner, Shannon Last, Suzanne Lauchaire, Diana Leddy, David Liben, Farren Liben, Liz Manolis, Jennifer Marin, Susannah Maynard, Cathy McGath, Emily McKean, Jane Miller, Rebecca Moore, Cathy Newton, Turi Nilsson, Julie Norris, Galemarie Ola, Michelle Palmieri, Meredith Phillips, Shilpa Raman, Tonya Romayne, Emmet Rosenfeld, Jennifer Ruppel, Mike Russoniello, Deborah Samley, Casey Schultz, Renee Simpson, Rebecca Sklepovich, Amelia Swabb, Kim Taylor, Vicki Taylor, Melissa Thomson, Lindsay Tomlinson, Melissa Vail, Keenan Walsh, Michelle Warner, Julia Wasson, Lynn Welch, Yvonne Guerrero Welch, Emily Whyte, Lynn Woods, and Rachel Zindler.

Early Adopters

The following early adopters provided invaluable insight and guidance for Wit & Wisdom:

- Bourbonnais School District 53 • Bourbonnais, IL
- Coney Island Prep Middle School • Brooklyn, NY
- Gate City Charter School for the Arts • Merrimack, NH
- Hebrew Academy for Special Children • Brooklyn, NY
- Paris Independent Schools • Paris, KY
- Saydel Community School District • Saydel, IA
- Strive Collegiate Academy • Nashville, TN
- Valiente College Preparatory Charter School • South Gate, CA
- Voyageur Academy • Detroit, MI

Design Direction provided by Alton Creative, Inc.

Project management support, production design and copyediting services provided by **ScribeConcepts.com**

Copyediting services provided by Fine Lines Editing

Product management support provided by Sandhill Consulting